超级眼镜

【美】劳拉·德里斯科尔◎著
【美】柏瑞·考特◎绘
范晓星◎译

天津出版传媒集团

新蕾出版社

S0-AKN-785

图书在版编目（CIP）数据

超级眼镜/（美）德里斯科尔（Driscoll,L.）著；（美）考特（Gott,B.）绘；范晓星译.
—天津：新蕾出版社，2013.7
（数学帮帮忙）
书名原文：Super Specs
ISBN 978-7-5307-5733-8

Ⅰ.①超…
Ⅱ.①德…②考…③范…
Ⅲ.①数学-儿童读物
Ⅳ.①O1-49

中国版本图书馆 CIP 数据核字(2013)第 062996 号
Super Specs by Laura Driscoll;
Illustrated by Barry Gott.
Text copyright ⓒ 2005 by Kane Press, Inc.
Illustrations copyright ⓒ 2005 by Barry Gott.
All rights reserved, including the right of reproduction in whole or in part in any
form. This edition published by arrangement with Kane Press, Inc. New York, NY,
represented by Lerner Publishing Group through The ChoiceMaker Korea Co.
Agency.
Simplified Chinese translation copyright ⓒ 2013 by New Buds Publishing House
(Tianjin) Limited Company
ALL RIGHTS RESERVED
本书中文简体版专有出版权经由中华版权代理中心授予新蕾出版社（天津）有
限公司。未经许可，不得以任何方式复制或抄袭本书的任何部分。
津图登字：02-2012-231

出版发行：天津出版传媒集团
　　　　　新蕾出版社
e-mail:newbuds@public.tpt.tj.cn
http://www.newbuds.cn
地　　址：天津市和平区西康路 35 号(300051)
出 版 人：马梅
电　　话：总编办 (022)23332422
　　　　　发行部 (022)23332676　23332677
传　　真：(022)23332422
经　　销：全国新华书店
印　　刷：北京盛通印刷股份有限公司
开　　本：787mm×1092mm　1/16
印　　张：2.5
版　　次：2013 年 4 月第 1 版　2013 年 7 月第 2 次印刷
定　　价：9.00 元

无处不在的数学

人民教育出版社小学数学室资深编辑　卢　江

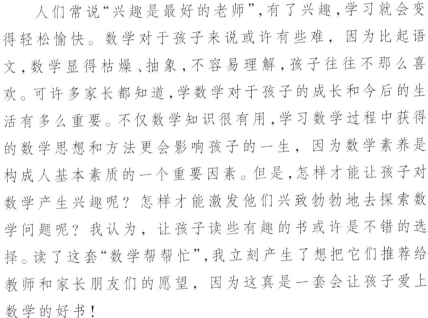

　　人们常说"兴趣是最好的老师",有了兴趣,学习就会变得轻松愉快。数学对于孩子来说或许有些难,因为比起语文,数学显得枯燥、抽象,不容易理解,孩子往往不那么喜欢。可许多家长都知道,学数学对于孩子的成长和今后的生活有多么重要。不仅数学知识很有用,学习数学过程中获得的数学思想和方法更会影响孩子的一生,因为数学素养是构成人基本素质的一个重要因素。但是,怎样才能让孩子对数学产生兴趣呢?怎样才能激发他们兴致勃勃地去探索数学问题呢?我认为,让孩子读些有趣的书或许是不错的选择。读了这套"数学帮帮忙",我立刻产生了想把它们推荐给教师和家长朋友们的愿望,因为这真是一套会让孩子爱上数学的好书!

　　这套有趣的图书从美国引进,全套共 25 册,原出版者是美国资深教育专家。每本书讲述一个孩子们生活中的故事,由故事中出现的问题自然地引入一个数学知识,然后通过运用数学知识解决问题。比如,从帮助外婆整理散落的纽扣引出分类,从为小狗记录藏骨头的地点引出空间方位,从办校报的活动讨论象形统计图的作用和制作方法，从为造一座糖果小屋找材料学习加减法的计算等等。故事素材全部来源于孩子们的真实生活，不是童话，不是幻想，而是鲜活的生活实例。正是这些发生在孩子身边的故事，让孩子们懂得，数学无处不在并且非常有用；这些鲜活的实例也使得抽象的概念更易于理解，更容易激发孩子学习数学的兴趣，让他们逐渐爱上数学。这样的教育思想和方法与我国近年来提倡的数学教育理念是十分吻合的！

这是一套适合5~8岁孩子阅读的书，书中的有趣情节和生动的插画可以将抽象的数学问题直观化、形象化，为孩子的思维活动提供具体形象的支持。如果亲子共读的话，家长可以带领孩子推测情节的发展，探讨解决难题的办法，让孩子在愉悦的氛围中学到知识和方法。

值得教师和家长朋友们注意的是，在每本书的后面，出版者还加入了"互动课堂"内容，一方面通过一些精心设计的活动让孩子巩固新学到的数学知识，进一步体会知识的含义和实际应用；另一方面帮助家长指导孩子阅读，体会故事中数学之外的道理，逐步提升孩子的阅读理解能力。

我相信孩子读过这套书后一定会明白，原来，数学不是烦恼，不是包袱，数学真能帮大忙！

我觉得我的新眼镜特别酷,可我弟弟艾迪可不这样想。"四眼!四眼!莫莉是个小四眼!"他唱道。

我们全家去超级乐园玩的路上,我说我们应该把艾迪留在家,可是我的父母不同意。

"艾迪!"爸爸说,"不许给莫莉起外号。"

"好啦,爸爸。"我对他说,"艾迪没惹我不高兴。"

不过，艾迪很让我生气，只不过我不想让他知道罢了。

所以，当他做鬼脸学我戴眼镜的样子时，我就假装没看见。

我盯着窗外，但并没有什么可看的，只有树木和5号出口的路牌。

艾迪在他的素描本上把我画成了一个可笑的漫画人物。我仍旧假装没看见。我们过了6号出口。

"爸爸！"我问道，"超级乐园是几号出口？"

"10号出口。"他答道。

唉！还有4个出口呢，艾迪还得折磨我那么久！

　　"嘿！"艾迪喊，"你戴着新眼镜的样子，多像这个太阳人啊！"他指着太阳人漫画书，还自作聪明地笑着对我说："可惜，你的眼镜不能带来 X 光视力！"

　　我恨得咬牙切齿。"7 号出口。"我对自己说。

艾迪把漫画书举到我眼前。我什么都没说，只是寻找着 8 号出口。出口之间的距离有多远啊？感觉好像总也开不到。

　　终于，我看到了路牌。

 根据这个规律，下一个出现的数字是几呢？

5,6,7,8,？

快点,9号出口!

要是我不快点离开这个总爱取笑我的艾迪,我就要爆炸了。

我深深地吸了一口气。

我一定要让他结束那些关于眼镜和 X 光视力的烦人言论!

　　突然,我有了个主意。

　　我要让艾迪觉得,我的眼镜真能带给我 X 光视力,那样他说话的腔调就会变了。

　　我想好了一套方案。虽然不会轻而易举,但我觉得我一定能成功。

我们在加油站停下车。妈妈带艾迪和我去买零食，爸爸给车加油。

　　"嘿，艾迪，"我说，"想玩考眼力的游戏吗？"比起拿我寻开心，艾迪还是更喜欢有人在车上陪他玩游戏。

　　"好极啦！"他说。

　　我们又上路了。我眯起眼睛,看着窗外。"我看到一个绿色的东西,上面写着数字9。"我说。

　　其实,我是假装的。所有的出口路牌都是绿色的,而且我知道9号出口就快到了。但是,艾迪不知道。沿路再开几英里才会到那个路牌呢。

　　"那儿有个9！"艾迪喊。他指的是一辆汽车的牌照。

　　"那不是绿色的。"我对他说，"接着找吧！"

　　我忍住不笑出来。

　　我们开过一个山坡，转了一个弯，过了一片玉米地。终于，艾迪看到了9号出口的路牌。

　　"它在这里！"他兴奋地大喊。

　　"对了！"我说，"就是这个。"

艾迪在他的座位上扭了几下。然后,他看着我:
"你怎么能够从加油站那里就看到这个路牌了呢?"
我耸耸肩膀说:"X 光视力。"
艾迪哼了一声。"哦,好吧。"他说。

几分钟后，我们来到 10 号出口，从高速公路上下来了。我们到超级乐园啦！

"这儿人太多了！"妈妈抱怨道。

　　妈妈说得没错。停车场几乎都满了。我们为
了找位置,开车绕了好几圈。
　　终于,我们在离停车场入口很远的地方找到
了一个位置。

"记住,我们把车停在了第 5 区。"爸爸指着我们身边一个高高的标志牌说道。

"咱们走吧!"艾迪说。

　　我们经过第 4 区的标志牌，然后是第 3 区和第 2 区。我们就要到入口了！

　　我从眼角处看到艾迪还皱着眉头呢。"你才没有 X 光视力呢。"他说，"这不可能！"

　　不过，听起来他并不肯定。

　　"不可能？"我笑着说。

　　我又想出了一个锦囊妙计。这次绝对能把艾
迪蒙住。

　　"看到那个了吗？"我指着前面的标志牌说，
"上面写的什么？"

　　艾迪眯起眼睛说："我从这儿看不到啊。"

根据这个规律，下一个出现的数字是几呢？

5,4,3,2,？

　　我推了推鼻梁上的眼镜："那个标志牌的另一面上写了一个大大的数字1。"

　　"你只是在猜测。"艾迪嘟囔着。

　　"我猜我们一会儿就能看见。"我对他说。

我们走过那个标志牌。艾迪发现我说对了。他觉得好惊讶，站住不走了。然后，他跑到爸爸妈妈跟前。

　　"我也可以有和莫莉一样的眼镜吗？"他央求道，"行吗？"

　　我忍不住咯咯直笑。好吧，艾迪上当了。不过，现在是该跟他揭开谜底的时候了。

我一直等到我们走到糖果村。"艾迪，其实这不是 X 光视力眼镜。高速公路边上出口的数字是有规律的。停车场的标志牌也是一个道理。"

"规律？"艾迪问，"那是什么意思？"

"你看街这边的房子。"我告诉他,"你看到每座房子上都有个号码吗?第一座房子上的号码是 2,下一个是 4,然后是 6,再然后是 8。所以,下一个是几号呢?"

根据这个规律,下一个出现的数字是几呢?

2,4,6,8,?

"10号？"艾迪说。

我们转过棒棒糖大树后，艾迪就看到了甜品大街10号。

"哇！"他大喊，"我也有X光视力啦！"

艾迪一整天都在寻找数字规律。
他找到了摩天轮上的数字规律。

根据这个规律,下一个出现的数字是几呢?

10,8,6,4,?

他发现了游船上的数字规律。

根据这个规律,下一个出现的数字是几呢?

1,3,5,7,?

然后，他又在游戏专区炫耀。

　　一个奖品前面没有数字。但是，当艾迪赢了时，他喊道："请给我7号奖品。"

　　尽管他看不到那个数字，但艾迪知道那个奖品的号码是什么。

回家的路上，艾迪再也不取笑我了。他在忙着喊出高速公路边上出口的数字。"5号出口，马上就到！"他说。

我们已经过了 8 号、7 号和 6 号出口。没错。艾迪真的明白数字规律的奥秘了。

但我还有最后一个小花招。

"妈妈!"我说,"咱们能在前面的冰激凌站停一下吗?"

"哪儿?"妈妈问,"我看到的只有高速公路啊。"

"等一会儿吧。"我告诉她。

"在那儿呢!"艾迪喊。

我们都看到了一个巨大的蛋卷冰激凌。

"下一站,冰激凌站!"爸爸预报道。

艾迪跟着我下了车。"这跟数字没关系！"他脱口而出，"你怎么知道冰激凌站在这里？"

我推了推鼻梁上的超级眼镜，耸了耸肩。

"很简单。"我说，"高速公路的每个出口都有一家！"

数字规律

你也可以变成一个给数字找规律的高手！

每组有规律的数字，都能找出运算的规则。有规律的数字就是根据这个运算规则排列的。

运算规则就是其中的奥秘。

运算规则例一：正着数 2 个数。
2,4,6,8

这样想:
2,3,4,5,
6,7,8

这样想:
9,8,7,6,
5,4,3

运算规则例二：倒着数 2 个数。
9,7,5,3

请看下面这 4 组有规律的数字，找出其中的运算规则。每组数字中的下一个数字是几呢？

1. 9,8,7,6,?   2. 1,3,5,7,?

3. 2,3,4,5,?   4. 10,8,6,4,?

规则 3：正着数 1 个数，下个数字是 6；规则 4：倒着数 2 个数，下个数字是 2。

规则 1：倒着数 1 个数，下个数字是 5；规则 2：正着数 2 个数，下个数字是 9。

答案:

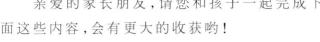

亲爱的家长朋友,请您和孩子一起完成下面这些内容,会有更大的收获哟!

提高阅读能力

• 阅读封面,包括书名、作者等内容。和孩子聊聊,为什么人们会戴眼镜?让孩子猜想故事是关于什么的?

• 和孩子一起读故事。艾迪为什么要捉弄莫莉?莫莉会有什么感觉?她决定怎么对付弟弟?

• 为什么莫莉决定不再逗艾迪了? 艾迪发现莫莉是在捉弄他时,他会有什么感觉?

巩固数学概念

- 使用第 32 页的内容来复习"数字规律"。为什么想要知道下一个数字该是什么,就应该先找到这组数字的运算规则?让孩子知道,这种运算规则意味着我们可以正着数几个数,也可以倒着数几个数。

- 请看第 11 页。莫莉怎么知道下一个出口是 9 的?在第 20～21 页上,莫莉怎么知道下一个数字是 1 的?

- 当艾迪知道数字规律的奥秘后,发生了什么事?莫莉和艾迪在哪些地方发现了数字规律?他们还有可能在什么地方找到有规律的数字?

- 请再读一遍这个故事。知道如何寻找数字规律,对莫莉和艾迪有什么帮助呢?和孩子聊聊,数字规律对我们的日常生活来说有什么帮助。比如,我们在超市里根据货架号码寻找商品,或者根据街道号码和门牌号码来找地址等等。

生活中的数学

- 寻找数字规律:鼓励孩子在家、商店、公园、教室等地方寻找有规律的数字。

- 请孩子自己设计一组故事中没有出现的有规律的数字。

SUPER SPECS

I think my new glasses are cool. But my brother Eddie doesn't. "Four eyes, four eyes! Molly has four eyes!" he sings.

We're on our way to Super Funland. I said we should leave Eddie home, but my parents wouldn't do it.

"Eddie!" Dad says. "Don't call Molly names."

"It's okay, Dad," I tell him. "Eddie's not bothering me."

But Eddie is bugging me. I just don't want him to know it.

So I pretend not to see him make googly-glasses faces.

I stare out the window, even though there's nothing to look at but trees and the sign for Exit 5.

Eddie draws a silly cartoon of me on his sketch pad. I just keep pretending not to notice. We pass Exit 6.

"Dad," I ask, "what's the Super Funland exit?"

"Exit 10," he replies.

Yikes! Four more exits to go—lots of time for Eddie to torture me.

"Hey!" Eddie yells. "You look like Solar Man with your new glasses." He points to his Solar Man comic book and gives me a wise-guy grin. "Too bad yours don't have x-ray vision!"

I grit my teeth. "There's Exit 7," I say to myself.

Eddie sticks his comic book right in my face. I don't say anything. I just look for Exit 8.

How far is it between exits? It feels like forever.

At last I see the sign.

Hurry up, Exit 9!

If I don't get away from smart-mouth Eddie soon, I'm going to explode.

I let out a big sigh.

I've got to make him quit all his annoying talk about glasses—and x-ray vision.

Then I get an idea.

I'll make Eddie think that my glasses do give me x-ray vision. That will change his tune.

I work out a plan. It won't be easy.

But I think I can pull it off.

We stop at a gas station. Mom takes Eddie and me to get snacks while Dad fills up the car.

"Hey, Eddie," I say, "want to play I Spy?" Eddie likes car games even more than teasing me.

"Great!" he says.

We drive off. I squint and look out the window. "I spy something green with the number 9 on it," I say.

I'm just pretending. All the exit signs are green—and I know Exit 9 is coming up. But Eddie doesn't. The sign is still a few miles down the road.

"There's a 9!" Eddie yells. He's pointing at a car's license plate.

"That's not green," I tell him. "Keep looking!"

I try not to laugh.

We drive over a hill, around a bend, and past a cornfield. Finally Eddie sees the sign for Exit 9.

"There it is!" he exclaims.

"Yep," I say. "That's it."

Eddie does a little dance in his seat. Then he looks at me. "How could you see that sign from all the way back at the gas station?"

I shrug. "X-ray vision."

Eddie snorts. "Yeah, right," he says.

A few minutes later we get to Exit 10 and pull off the highway. We're at Super Funland!

"It's so crowded," Mom complains.

Mom's right. The parking lot is almost full. We drive around and around, looking for a space.

At last we find one—far away from the park entrance.

"Remember—we're parked in Section 5," Dad says. He points to a tall sign near our spot.

"Let's go!" says Eddie.

We walk past the signs for Section 4, then 3, then 2. We're almost at the entrance!

Out of the corner of my eye, I see Eddie frowning. "You don't have x-ray vision," he says. "It's impossible."

But he doesn't sound so sure.

"Impossible?" I say, and smile.

I've got another trick up my sleeve. This one is sure to freak Eddie out.

"See that?" I point to the sign up ahead. "What does it say?"

Eddie squints. "I can't read it from here."

I push my glasses up on my nose.

"There's a big number 1 on the other side of that sign."

"You're just guessing," Eddie grumbles.

"I guess we'll see," I tell him.

We walk by the sign. Eddie sees I'm right. He's so amazed, he stops in his tracks. Then he runs up to Mom and Dad.

"Can I get glasses like Molly's?" he begs. "Please?"

I can't help giggling. Eddie fell for my trick, all right. But it's time to let him in on the joke.

I wait until we get to Candy Village. "These aren't really x-ray glasses, Eddie," I say.

"There's a pattern to the exit numbers on the highway. Same goes for the parking-lot signs."

"A pattern?" asks Eddie. "What does that mean?"

"Check out the houses on this side of the street," I tell him. "See how each one has a number? That first house is number 2. The next is 4. Then 6. Then 8. So what will the next one be?"

"Number 10?" says Eddie.

Right after we pass the lollipop tree, Eddie spots number 10 Sweet Tooth Lane.

"Wow!" he shouts. "I have x-ray vision, too!"

Eddie looks for number patterns all day.

He finds them on the Ferris wheel.

He spots them at the boat ride.

And he shows off again at the game arcade.

One prize doesn't have a number. But when Eddie wins, he calls out, "Seven, please!"

Eddie knows what the prize number is, even though he can't see it.

Eddie doesn't tease me on the ride home. He's too busy calling out exit numbers. "Exit 5, coming up!" he says.

We've already passed Exits 8, 7, and 6. Yep. Eddie really has the hang of number patterns.

But I have one last trick.

"Mom," I say. "Can we stop at the Ice Cream Depot up ahead?"

"Where?" asks Mom. "All I see is highway."

"Just wait," I tell her.

"There it is!" Eddie yells.

We can all see the giant cone.

"Next stop, Ice Cream Depot!" Dad announces.

Eddie follows me out of the car. "That was no number trick!" he blurts out. "How did you know the Depot would be here?"

I push my super specs up on my nose and shrug.

"Easy," I say. "There's been one at every exit!"